This book belongs to:

_____

_____

_____

GOODWORD

Illustrated by Achla Anand
First published 2004
Reprinted 2013
© Goodword Books 2013

Goodword Books
1, Nizamuddin West Market, New Delhi-110 013
Tel. 9111-4182-7083, 4652-1511
Fax: 9111-4565-1771
email: info@goodwordbooks.com
www.goodwordbooks.com, www.goodword.net

IB Publisher Inc.
81 Bloomingdale Rd, Hicksville, NY 11801, USA
Tel. 516-933-1000, Fax: 516-933-1200
Toll Free: 1-888-560-3222
email: info@ibpublisher.com, www.ibpublisher.com

Non-Profit Bookstore
Talim-ul-Islam Community Center
86 Rivalda Road, Toronto ON M9M 2M8, Canada
Tel. 416-740-7844
email: lugatulquran@hotmail.com, www.LQToronto.com

Islamic Vision Ltd.
434 Coventry Road, Small Heath
Birmingham B10 0UG, U.K.
Tel. 121-773-0137, Fax: 121-766-8577
e-mail: info@ipci-iv.co.uk, www.islamicvision.co.uk

Printed in India

FAVOURITE TALES FROM THE
QURAN

TWO TALES:
Two Sons of Adam
Travels of Ibrahim

Saniyasnain Khan

GOODWORD

Two Sons of Adam

Long long ago, when Allah created
the beautiful world, He decided to create
a human being, so He created the first
man, Adam ﷺ. Allah also created the
first woman, Hawwa (Eve), as a helper
and loving companion to Adam ﷺ. The
Prophet Adam ﷺ and his wife happily
began their lives on the earth.

Imagine what the earth would have been like at that time, when there were no human beings apart from them. No pollution, no noise, no crowds... There was peace and great harmony everywhere. The Prophet Adam ﷺ and Hawwa were blessed with two sons, Habil (Abel) and Qabil (Cain). When they grew up, Habil, the younger brother, became a shepherd. He herded sheep, goats and other animals.

The elder brother, Qabil, worked as a farmer, tilling the fields. One day both decided to make a sacrifice to please their Lord. Habil took the best of his flock, while Qabil brought his crops. They usually laid out the sacrifice in a high place. If a fire came down from heaven and burnt the offering to ashes, it was a sign that Allah was pleased with it.

Suddenly a spark of light flashed and burnt Habil's offering to ashes. This showed that Allah accepted his sacrifice, but rejected Qabil's sacrifice. Qabil's failure made him hate and feel jealous of his younger brother. He felt it was Habil's fault that he was put to shame.

Habil tried to explain to Qabil why his sacrifice had not been accepted: "In your heart you have no fear of Allah," Habil said to his brother. "That is why Allah did not accept your sacrifice."

But, instead of agreeing and feeling sorry for his mistake, Qabil felt hurt at being disgraced and insulted. His face darkened with anger and his heart became hardened: "No," cried Qabil, "I will kill you!"

At this threat from his elder brother, Habil did not shout back. He just said calmly: "Even if you raise your hand to kill me, I will not fight back, for I fear Allah, the Lord of the Worlds." These fine words spoken by his younger brother could not calm Qabil, as he was blinded by jealousy and puffed up with arrogance and anger.

Qabil's anger got the better of him and he killed his innocent brother Habil. But no sooner had he done this horrifying deed than he began to change. Seeing the blood spilled all around the motionless body of his younger brother, Qabil's anger slowly cooled.

Now he realized what a big mistake he had made. He had acted in haste, he had done something vile, and now, thinking about it, he felt very sorry. For hours he sat nearby, shamed and grief-stricken, looking down at his brother's mute, blood-spattered body: "Now I have killed my brother," said Qabil to himself in deep sorrow, "but what shall I do with his body?"

Then Allah sent a raven, which landed
on the ground near the body. The raven
began to scratch the ground to tell Qabil
that he should bury his brother's dead
body under the earth.

"Woe is me!" cried Qabil helplessly. "I am worse even than this raven, for I cannot hide my brother's corpse." Qabil felt his meanness all the more so, because even a raven could teach him a lesson. The moral of this story is that two believers should never fight with each other. Even if one of them is bent on fighting, the other one, like the obedient Habil, should never fight back.

The Quran says: "If anyone killed a person—except as punishment for murder or other corruption in the land—it shall be looked upon as if he had killed all mankind. And whoever saved a human life, shall be looked upon as if he had saved all mankind."

Travels of Ibrahim

SURAH IBRAHIM 14:36-41, AL-ANKABUT 29:26-27

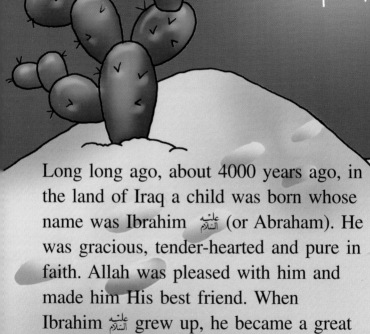

Long long ago, about 4000 years ago, in the land of Iraq a child was born whose name was Ibrahim عليه السلام (or Abraham). He was gracious, tender-hearted and pure in faith. Allah was pleased with him and made him His best friend. When Ibrahim عليه السلام grew up, he became a great prophet, and preached the truth and Allah's message in his country.

Later he travelled to Syria, Palestine and
Egypt. When a beautiful son was born
to his wife, Hajar (or Hagar), Ibrahim
عليه السلام was ordered by Allah to travel
towards what we now know as Makkah
along with his wife and the little child,
whose name was Ismail (or Ishmael).

19

They all travelled for a long time till they reached a lonely, barren valley, near two small hills called Safa and Marwah. The Prophet Ibrahim ﷺ asked his wife to stay near one of the hills along with the baby Ismail, and started to go away.

His wife protested, "Why are you leaving us alone here? Are you leaving us here to die?" But Ibrahim ﷿ replied, "My Lord has commanded me to do this." Then Hajar, breathing a sigh of relief, said: "If Allah has ordered you to do so, then He will not let us die."

After a while, little Ismail began to cry becuse he was thirsty. But there was not a single drop of water to drink.

Hajar ran helplessly from one hill to another, but there was no water, nor was there any human being nearby to give her any.

As the baby was crying desperately with thirst and the mother was running from one hill to another, Allah caused a miracle to take place—a spring gushed forth beneath the feet of Ismail عليه السلام.

When Hajar saw this from a distance, she shouted, "Zamzam"—the sound made by rushing water in the Babylonian language. Hajar came running and gave some fresh spring water to the thirsty child to drink. And so his life was saved.

This spring became famous later on and was called by the name of Zamzam. Ismail ﷺ and his mother began to live in the valley.

Because of the Zamzam spring, more people gradually came to settle there, slowly building up a small town, which was later called Makkah.

From time to time Ibrahim ﷺ would
visit Makkah to meet his family,
especially to see his young Ismail
growing up in the beautiful surroundings
of nature—in a new town in a lovely
valley surrounded by hills, away from
the crowded cities where the people at
that time were mostly idol-worshippers.

The moral of this story is that believers who, despite their hardships, follow the path of Allah, will find that, Allah will remain with them and help them in miraculous ways, just as the child Ismail ﷺ was saved by the miracle of the Zamzam spring.

ﷺ *Alayhis Salam* 'May peace be upon him.' The customary blessing on the prophets.